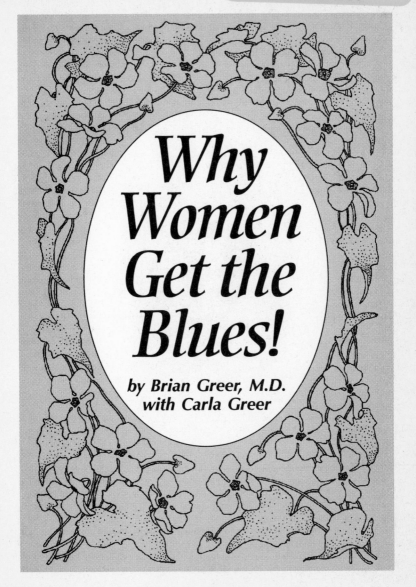

Why Women Get the Blues!

by Brian Greer, M.D.
with Carla Greer

WHAT ARE THE BLUES?

The "blues" are the ache in your heart when you know that something isn't quite right with your life. The blues are all the frustrations, the fears, the dullness, the sense of loss you may feel as you make it through each day and provide for others.

The blues can be very damaging. They rob you of the spirit and strength to seek happiness, growth and inner healing. And they make everything seem so bleak that it's easy to give in and feel there's no way out.

You're not alone. Despite the happy faces the women around you may be wearing, many of them are suffering, too. Examples are everywhere, on TV and in the movies. And, like you, they may think that having the blues is a sign of their inner worthlessness or a kind of self-pity they're not entitled to feel. So they hide it.

Do any of these statements describe you?

❀ You feel like you're just going through the motions of your life without any pleasure or sense of purpose.

❀ You feel like romance has left your relationship.

❀ You were often criticized as a child. Now you feel you must earn love through being sweet and selfless.

❀ You can't stand up for yourself when you're mistreated.

❀ You – or your partner – don't think your feelings count.

❀ You have given up the most precious parts of yourself, or the things you love, to take care of other people.

❀ You feel overwhelmed by resentment or guilt.

❀ You're not sleeping or eating properly.

❀ You are tired, bored or sad...drained of your life force.

❀ You feel a lot of anger. But you're afraid to express it.

❀ You often feel no one understands you.

❀ One unkind word can tear down your self-esteem.

WHAT THIS BOOK CAN DO FOR YOU

Make no mistake; the blues are real. The good news is that the solutions are real, too.

We've organized this book by the 12 main causes of the blues. As you'll discover, these causes often stem from ideas about yourself that you've learned from society, from your parents, your husband...your relationships.

These messages tell you how you're supposed to act and think. And you may feel – as many women do – torn between your own needs and these often conflicting messages.

Our culture taught you to be feminine: agreeable and self-sacrificing. Now, you're being told to be independent, assertive and motivated. You're left without a clear idea of what you should do. You doubt your choices and are full of guilt and resentments – no matter which path you choose.

This book will give you practical, tested advice on what you can do on your own to banish your blues.

You'll find a step-by-step program to improve your self-esteem, gain personal power and find out how to put passion, romance and meaning back into your life.

You'll also learn how to feel good about yourself and build up powerful defenses against an exhausting workload – and destructive relationships.

REMEMBER:

However you're feeling today, next week can be different! All you have to do is find the courage to change. Trust in your inner strength or a higher power.

This book will show you the way.

WHY DO WOMEN GET THE BLUES?

There are actually 12 different answers to this single question. We've given each one a chapter, complete with ways to overcome the problem.

They are titled:

1. YOU CAN'T PLEASE EVERYONE!

PLEASER: Mary Richards in *The Mary Tyler Moore Show*

"People pleasing" is the desire to make others happy, even if it means ignoring your own needs.

At a very deep level, it's also the unconscious giving away of your power to others. You let other people (your husband, boss or friends) – and how they feel about you at any given moment – determine how you feel about yourself. And you can only feel good about yourself when these people think of you as a perfect, giving, selfless woman who puts others first.

People pleasing shows up in the choices you make in life, your relationships, the way you talk and the things you worry about. It can lead to the blues and drain you of your own life force.

ARE YOU A PEOPLE PLEASER?

1. Are you afraid of being seen as a strong, assertive or aggressive woman who cares about her own needs?

2. Would you rather be liked than respected?

3. In your friendships, do you see a pattern of giving more than receiving? Have you often been hurt and betrayed by friends?

4. When you talk, do you tend to use a little girl voice that doesn't come from deep in the diaphragm?

5. When asked to do a favor, do you quickly rush to say "yes" – without thinking about how the extra work is going to affect you?

6. Do you find that you never have time for exercise, creative and fun activities or hobbies?

7. Do you worry a lot about how others think of you?

If you are a people pleaser, don't think it's because of any character weakness. It's a deep-rooted pattern of thinking that begins in childhood.

A child gains a sense of who she is during her first few years of life. Her parents let her know through smiles and eye contact that she is an independent, important, lovable person who is cherished for who she is.

But when parents somehow send the message that the child is supposed to live out THEIR dreams or to fulfill THEIR emotional needs, the girl's sense of herself changes. She begins to feel, even before the age of three, that she is only worthwhile based on *how well she pleases her parents and makes them happy and whole.*

Why do more women than men turn out to be pleasers? Mainly, it's because society reinforces the pattern throughout a woman's life. Women learn through movies, ads and real life that their self-esteem – how much they value themselves – should be tied to their success at nurturing, or taking care of, others. Some of the things you may have learned that tie into this are:

❀ It's okay to find a good career as long as it's a helping profession (for example: nursing or teaching).

❀ Do well at your job and in school, but don't do better than your husband. (In other words, don't do TOO well!)

❀ You can work hard in your profession, but your husband and family must come first.

❀ Of course you should exercise and take care of yourself, but first make sure the house is spotless, everyone else's needs are taken care of, and it doesn't take up time you could be using to help others.

Something else critical happens during this period. If the parents are emotionally unhealthy, the child will deny that anything is wrong with them. Think about it. Nothing is more frightening to a helpless child than to imagine her parents are emotionally unbalanced and therefore unable to take care of her.

Instead, the child will believe that the parent is perfect and that SHE has the problem! You can see how this sets off a life-long thinking pattern in which the woman sees herself as unworthy and sees everyone else as okay.

As a result, the grown-up woman is always looking for someone to play out the role of parent and tell her (through words or actions) that she is good and deserves to be loved. So, in order to get this approval that she didn't get when she was young, the woman pleases anybody who may fit that role. This could be her husband or partner, friend, boss, or anyone in a position of authority.

There are endless ways in which your life may suffer from people pleasing. Maybe you put your husband through school, had to quit school yourself to do it, and now you feel stuck in a job that doesn't offer you the excitement or money you need. You may want to take more of a high-power position at work, but you're afraid your husband or family will resent the additional hours you'll have to put into it. Or you may see others at work – people you give ideas and advice to – get promoted, while you're passed aside because others see you as a nice, selfless person who will accept the lower pay and status.

People pleasing takes its worst toll on personal relationships. You've probably learned the ironic truth that being too nice doesn't work. Extra kindness to your husband won't be paid back. What's worse, it might even cause you to lose his respect!

Debbie, a nurse at my hospital, told me, "I'm always seen as a "foul-weather friend." When a friend is depressed and needs a shoulder to cry on, she runs to me. When my husband is going through a bad time, I'll stay up all night with him, giving him love and support. But when things are going well for a friend or my husband, I notice they are colder to me, less interested in giving me their time."

A patient of mine, Laura, realized that she was set up by her husband to be the very thing he hated, and she let it happen because she wanted so much to please him.

"Dan begged me to give up my great job in public relations. So I did. He told me he wanted a beautiful old-fashioned marriage. The first year, things were great. I loved all that time for myself.

"But by the second year, the days became endlessly long waiting for him to come home. He would get defensive when I'd ask him what time he was leaving work, and he started accusing me of being a nag. When he'd get home, I would have to search for things to talk about. He was starting to get bored with my conversation. He even asked me once what I did all day, as if I were lazy. And he stopped complimenting me.

"At a Christmas party last year, I overheard him praising another woman in the public relations department at his office for doing such a wonderful job, and I flew into a rage. I could have done a better job than she did, and instead I was this boring housewife. Why? Because of him!"

Like Debbie or Laura, you might be caught in a vicious cycle. You give of yourself to your husband or your friends. You mean well, and all you want back in return is their love and respect. But sadly, the more giving you are, the less they give of themselves to you.

REMEMBER:

Except in the case of your children, anytime you put someone else's needs in front of your own, you are bound to become resentful or angry at yourself.

GROWING OUT OF PEOPLE PLEASING

People pleasing is about powerlessness. Strange as it may seem, you try to gain power, control and self-esteem by giving away your power to others – in the hope they'll give you something back!

The only solution to people pleasing is *self-empowerment*.

We're going to take a look at eight different ways to get a strong sense of your own power:

1) KNOW WHAT YOU STAND FOR

All through nursing school, Cindy was very outspoken about patient care. While some of her classmates were busy joking around, she would bring the discussion back to caring for others.

Despite her busy schedule at the hospital, Cindy organized several fund-raisers for a children's hospice and spent extra time at the cancer unit. She would challenge any classmate who made a cynical comment about a patient.

One student in particular, Mark, was annoyed at her for her strong beliefs, and often put her down for them. Then just before graduation, Mark asked Cindy if they could talk. He needed advice about his ill sister.

Cindy asked why he chose her out of all people, given his obvious dislike for her.

He answered, "Because you know who you are, you actually stand for something in this world."

Knowing what you stand for, then living your life according to it, is what gives you integrity and purpose. It's harder than it appears at first glance. To really know what you stand for means sifting through all the values and philosophies you grew up with and learned later as an adult. You also need to learn more about the world around you and yourself. Although it's important to leave yourself flexible enough to change and grow, you'll want to select values that can stand up to the test of time and the challenges you'll face.

Whether you can then live by these philosophies is the test of both the strength of your beliefs and your self-esteem.

We all know people who talk about how much they care about endangered species, or their religious/spiritual practices, or helping the homeless, or their children. But when you look at how they actually live their lives, how they spend their time and money, you get a very different picture of what they really care about.

These people always seem ready to take on the changing values of their current environment, or the people they're with, in order to get outside approval. This is called an "as if" or "chameleon" personality, named after the reptile that changes its color.

Years ago, a wise psychiatrist told me, "To be a good therapist, you must be able to take the occasional anger of your patients." This applies also to anyone who wants a life of integrity. Your self-esteem must be strong enough to weather the occasional disapproval of others.

WHAT CAN YOU DO?

- ❁ Take a stand on issues that are important to you.

- ❁ The key is to decide what is important to you. It might be God or a higher power, destiny and immortality, the sacredness of life, the value of children, priorities in child care, or one of an endless number of beliefs.

- ❁ Develop your own strong voice and a day-to-day life that reflects your beliefs. Learn to get your approval from within.

- ❁ People may disagree with you. But if you act on your beliefs, they'll respect you more in the end. And more importantly, you'll respect yourself.

- ❁ What people call the "midlife crisis" is the period when a middle-aged person reviews her life and has the painful realization that she didn't have either the courage or the conviction to live up to her beliefs. But you can escape the midlife blues if you make changes now.

REMEMBER:

Never think your beliefs make you better than anyone else. If they're a strong part of you, you won't have to change or preach to others.

2) SET FIRM LIMITS & PERSONAL BOUNDARIES

You may believe that you don't let other people take advantage of you. But if you often find yourself in situations in which you're slowly pulled into accepting hurtful or unfair behavior, you may unknowingly be showing other people that you're willing to be manipulated.

The best way to avoid being manipulated is to make up a list of limits that you will never allow yourself to violate, even when your self-esteem is low and you feel the need for approval. Try the "one day at a time" approach. The next time someone asks you to do something that goes outside of your "limits," and then he or she makes you feel so guilty or lacking in self-esteem that you feel the urge to give in, tell yourself, "Just for today, I'm going to stick to my boundaries. I haven't completely changed my personality. Maybe tomorrow I'll give in." Then, when tomorrow comes, tell yourself the same thing!

A friend, Chaya, told me about a time she was asked to serve on a committee that was to meet only occasionally at night. That fit her schedule just fine, so she agreed.

About a week later, at a meeting that Chaya wasn't able to attend, the other committee members decided among themselves that since Chaya didn't have children, she would be the perfect candidate to do some extra committee work during the daytime hours.

When the chairman called Chaya to ask her, her first impulse was to grudgingly agree. After all, everyone else had bus pickups and car pools to worry about. She didn't want the committee members to think she was lazy or selfish.

"But then I did something for the first time," she says. "I went deep inside of myself to check out whether it felt right to take on this burden, and it didn't. I felt I was not adequately respected. So I told the chairman 'No.'"

Here's a sample list of boundaries and limits one woman wrote for herself. The items I've starred are absolute musts for any woman.

* ✻ I will not allow myself or my children to be physically, sexually or verbally abused.
* ✻ I will have sex only when I choose, and only when I'm feeling loved and valued.
* ✻ I will accept nothing less than total faithfulness from my husband.
* ✻ I will not agree to do anything that takes time away from my caring for my health.
* I will not do more than my fair share of the housework.

3) BE KIND, BUT DON'T "ENABLE"

While you're working on self-growth, it's easy to find yourself becoming as cold and uncaring as those who hurt you. That's because when you think of strong behavior, you often think of those people. But becoming cold is a sign you've actually given up your power, because you've given up your "inner core of light" – which is your true strength.

Instead, on a day-to-day basis, start separating kind behavior (which comes from the healthy, powerful part of you) from what is called "enabling" behavior.

Enabling behavior is anything that allows someone else to get away with something that DESERVES to bring negative consequences. An addicted gambler DESERVES to lose money. An alcoholic DESERVES to get in trouble at work. A procrastinator DESERVES to get a bad grade in college if he doesn't study.

They deserve it, not because they're bad people and should be punished, but because that's the only way they will learn and change. If you keep rescuing another person from the consequences of his unhealthy behavior, you are hurting both him and yourself. You're giving both of you a "quick fix" which allows you to feel you're in control of a scary situation that threatens your safety. (Maybe you were in a similar situation as a child. Think about it.)

But remember that control is temporary and make-believe. The more you enable, the smaller the chance that the other person will permanently change. You'll also never get the appreciation and love you're looking for because the other person will end up resentful toward you.

If you're enabling someone in your life, here's what you can do:

1) Attend Al-Anon meetings. They're held in every city nationwide.

2) Detach from this person with love and put your energy into your own needs. This often gives her the jolt she needs and will increase her respect for you.

3) Stop believing that you must stay in control to keep everything going well. Remember, your best thinking and best attempts at control got you where you both are now!

It will help to close the reins even tighter on your own boundaries and limits. Be sure you don't do anything that goes against your ethics, rights or needs. The best thing you can do for the other person is communicate your own inner strength and light.

4) TAKE CONTROL OF YOUR BEHAVIOR, BUT NO MORE. YOU'RE NOT RESPONSIBLE FOR EVERYTHING THAT HAPPENS

There is only one thing we each really control...our own actions. There is nothing we can do, however, to ENSURE the outcome of those actions. We can't make someone love us, we can't make someone think we're a good person, we can't necessarily make someone do what we want them to do. In short, we are powerless over other people.

Despite all this, think about how much energy, worry and guilt you've probably put into thinking about other people's actions and reactions to you! And often, in an effort to force a good outcome (an outcome that you often don't get anyway), you do something that either goes against your principles or robs you of your dignity and power.

Julie got very friendly with Susan at a PTA meeting. She invited her and her husband for dinner the following Friday night.

Julie and her husband did all they could to be gracious hosts. When Susan failed to call to say thank you, Julie began to worry that Susan didn't have a good time.

She lay awake at night wondering what she did wrong at the dinner party. Then she remembered that Susan had mentioned that it was her birthday the following week. The next day, Julie bought a little gift for Susan's birthday and left it in her mailbox, along with a note offering to get together on her birthday.

When Julie saw Susan the next day at their daughters' school, Susan gave her a cold thank you for the gift, said that she already had birthday plans and walked away.

Julie stood there feeling shocked, hurt and humiliated. She had given away her power to Susan, had cared about Susan's response to her, and now felt terrible about herself.

Doing the right thing according to your convictions is the best any of us can do. Obsessing about what happens next gives someone else the power over our self-esteem.

REMEMBER:

When you need other people's approval to give you self-esteem, you're bound to get hurt.

A good rule to follow is: Devote time, thought and energy to your own behavior. Make sure that your actions are in keeping with what you stand for. Know that you did the right thing. THEN LET IT GO.

5) TAKE MORE RESPONSIBILITY FOR YOUR LIFE

THERE ARE TWO WAYS OF LOOKING AT YOUR LIFE

1) Most of what has happened to me is the result of poor parenting, lack of money, the terrible values of our society, an uncaring husband, disobedient children and cruel in-laws. If it weren't for these problems, I could achieve my dreams.

2) Painful things have happened to me which I handled as well as I could at the time. Many hurdles

were put in my path for me to overcome, and I don't know why. But the problems I've faced weren't unfair accidents of birth or fate, and I wasn't left powerless.

Instead, they are part of what created the richness and fullness of who I am today. They are also part of my life's work and have shaped my understanding of my spiritual purpose. And because these problems were specifically created for my personal growth (by God, my higher power, or my own psychic energies), I am able to deal with them and, in so doing, change my life.

No matter what our philosophy of life, we can never know for certain that we hold the absolute truth. There usually remains within each of us a small voice that wonders and doubts. That is healthy, especially if we use that questioning voice to keep us from being self-righteous about our beliefs.

Since none of us can know absolute truth in this world, the best we can do is choose a system of belief that helps us become happier, healthier people.

The second way of looking at your life, as I've described above, may seem a bit mystical and spiritual. It is. One thing that is clear to me after years of clinical work is that not only are we here for a purpose, but everyone has a strong part to play in what happens to them.

There are many ways in which you or your higher power can influence events in your life.

When a new patient named Samantha came to see me, she complained that her husband was always criticizing her and eroding her self-esteem. Slowly, she came to see that she was in part responsible for her husband's behavior. She went home with a different attitude. While walking through her front door, she repeated affirmations, or positive statements, to herself about her ability, goodness and kindness. She told herself she had no control over her husband's angry comments, which were really coming from his own insecurity. What's more, she would not get drawn into his games. All her begging and arguing was never going to get him to stop because his anger wasn't really about her to begin with.

Next, she told herself that her higher power wanted her to be in this situation for a purpose. Her job was to figure out the purpose. Could it be that she needed to learn to keep her self-esteem intact despite what he said about her? Could it be so that she could get in touch with old fears of abandonment and rejection? Or could it be to learn that she doesn't have to stay in an abusive relationship?

During that week, Samantha sorted through those questions. She stopped getting upset about what her husband said to her. She realized she wasn't a victim and could take responsibility for her reactions.

After a week of this new attitude, Samantha found to her astonishment that her husband began to change on his own. The stronger and more powerful she felt (even though she didn't tell him so in words), the more he picked up on it and began to respect her.

6) LET GO OF GUILT AND RESENTMENT

Guilt and resentments rob you of your power. If you do something wrong, feeling guilty afterward is a healthy response that shows you have a conscience. It's especially productive if it leads you to repair the hurt or damage you caused. It can also motivate you to do the right thing...to call your grandmother on Mother's Day or to buy your co-worker lunch during a stressful week.

But guilt should never *take the place* of such positive action, especially when it's experienced merely as a result of childhood messages.

Where does all the guilt come from?

1) Messages from parents that they were a failure.

EXAMPLE: *Children whose parents divorce may blame themselves for the divorce. This guilt can last a lifetime.*

2) Mistakes made earlier in life that have altered their feelings about themselves on a deep level.

EXAMPLE: *A woman who "slept around" may spend the next 20 years trying to undo the shame and guilt.*

3) Worries that taking care of their own needs is selfish and bad. Also, the feeling that they don't have the right to feel happy or have fun.

Sara was always feeling helpless and guilty. While growing up, her father was respected in the community but a raging alcoholic at home. He would humiliate, hit and scream at his children.

As the oldest, Sara learned from her mother that it was her job to make her father happy and protect her younger sisters from him. But Sara was too scared to stand up to him and too angry to play the role of the affectionate daughter. All she could do was grow numb.

When Sara turned 16, her mother developed severe pneumonia. Sara was so angry at her mother for never having protected the family from her father that she barely helped to take care of her.

Now that Sara is 36 and happily married with her own children, she has a hard time feeling much pleasure. She feels guilty she didn't protect her sisters, guilty she didn't love her mother enough to take care of her, and now guilty that her guilt is making her less than an ideal mother. Sara's husband can't understand why she always has the blues when their life is so good.

Q.

What vitamins can I take to relieve my depression?

A.

Here's a useful program to try after first consulting your doctor:

Amino Acids:
Amino acids aid the production of neurotransmitters, the chemical messengers in the brain. They may increase blood pressure, so do consult your doctor. Take daily: L-phenylalanine (500 to 1,000 mg); tyrosine (500 to 1,000 mg).

Antioxidants:
They support the immune system. Take daily: Ester C (2,000-4,000 mg); beta carotene (75,000 IU); vitamin E (400 mg); selenium (150 mcg).

B complex:
Also known as "stress" or "nerve" vitamins. Sufferers need more because the body uses them up to counteract stress and depression. Be sure to include vitamin B6 which manufactures the neurotransmitters. Take 50 mg daily.

Choline:
Either by itself or in the form of lecithin. It increases the amount of the neurotransmitter acetylcholine in the brain. Follow the directions on the package.

As in Sara's case, too much guilt is self-defeating. And even though guilt comes out of the caring, moral part of you, it actually becomes self-serving. How? Well, it makes you think that you're becoming a better person through suffering. But pointless suffering helps nobody. It doesn't help you get over your self-esteem problems. Nor does it make up for any harm you may have actually caused. Not only does it not heal wounds, but it destroys the spirit, and with it, the strength to heal.

Resentment against people who have hurt you is equally draining. All of us have been disturbed by hurtful behavior. But letting yourself get overloaded with resentments – even when you really believe that you DESERVE to feel resentful – takes power AWAY from you and gives it to the very people who harmed you.

As with guilt, resentment can actually make you ill. Studies show a strong link between cancer and other diseases to guilt, resentments and held-back anger.

EIGHT STEPS TO LOSE YOUR GUILT

A) Begin by writing your life story. Start from as early as you can remember. First memories are usually very important. Think about all the feelings about yourself that you got from your parents, and reflect upon these in your writing. As you go back through your life, include every event and relationship that shaped your self-image in some way. Include both your regrets and your peak moments.

B) When you're finished, read your story aloud to yourself or to a trusted friend. Look for patterns. Were you made to feel guilty a lot? Did you take on guilt and responsibility for things you couldn't possibly control? Are there people you have hurt who you're still

25

obsessing about but haven't done anything about?

C) Make a list of the people that you've actually harmed. Be sure, if applicable, to include your children. They are more vulnerable to being hurt than anyone else.

D) Next to each name, write down a positive action you can take to try to make things right if you haven't already done so.

E) Here are some suggestions: a face-to-face apology; do something kind for the person (even without their knowing you did it); if a direct action isn't possible, do something kind for someone else in their memory or honor such as giving to a charity or doing public service.

> A friend was feeling very guilty for leaving her husband which deprived her children of a full-time father. Although she had no choice but to leave him because he had had several affairs, she couldn't stop herself from obsessing over her guilt.

F) Next, make another list of the types of guilt you feel as a result of the way you were brought up. These are the negative images that are part of you and with which you've hurt yourself. Some of these may be: using drugs in high school; having a destructive love affair; making a poor career or life choice.

G) Finally, list things you feel guilty about that were not in your control.

H) Next to all of these, write a positive action you will make to yourself.

In making amends to yourself, you have to be creative. You can decide, for example, to symbolically (and perhaps physically) repair the damage of drug use by going on a new program of health. You can remedy a poor career choice by going back to school. You will also need to forgive yourself, which is nothing more than giving yourself the same love and compassion you would give to others.

One of the many things that Sara felt guilty about was her inability to stand up to her father when he would get in a rage. She felt that her fearfulness and inability to protect her sisters was a sign of an inner weakness. She felt guilty over being so powerless.

As an amend to herself, Sara enrolled both herself and her daughter in a karate class. It was a way of showing herself that she now was a physically powerful person. And it was a way of transforming something painful in her life into something empowering in her daughter's life.

In the future, when you start to feel guilty, step back and ask the question, "Have I actually done something wrong, or are these old tapes playing in my head?" If the answer is old tapes, fight it off by working on your self-esteem. (See the next section on low self-esteem.) If you've hurt someone else or yourself, show courage and power by taking positive action. Then let go of it.

HERE'S WHAT TO DO WITH RESENTMENTS

If you haven't already done so, write the life story described in the previous section. Make a point of highlighting all the people who have hurt you or damaged your sense of self. Then make a list of all those people you resent, along with what they did to you. Next to that, write down what you think each person's motives might have been.

> **The following is an excerpt from the list of Jacqui, a woman with a long history of abusive friends:**
>
> **Person:** Rebecca
> **What She Did:** Used our friendship to go out with my boyfriend's best friend in high school, then dropped me when they broke up
> **Possible Motive:** Desperation, insecurity
>
> **Person:** Steve
> **What He Did:** Emotionally abusive during our four-year relationship
> **Possible Motive:** Anger toward mother/inability to love
>
> **Person:** Boss
> **What She Did:** Severely and unfairly critical
> **Possible Motive:** Jealous

Now study your list with as open a mind as possible. Focus on the fact that many of your injuries came out of the OTHER person's weaknesses, fears and problems. Understand it's nothing more than a reflection of them, not of you. Try to understand your part in the drama. Did any of these events happen because you allowed them to?

Once you've put everything in a clearer perspective, it's time to weaken the power of these resentments. You can do this by taking action yourself.

For as many offenses on the list as you need, think of

some activity that will take you out of the role of suffering victim. The easiest, most productive way to handle a resentment is to say something to the offender. This is best done in a calm, firm voice, and can go something like this: "I just want you to know that when you did X, I felt Y. I have been wondering whether you meant to make me feel this way. Maybe we can clear this up?"

But words are not always possible. If the offender is your boss, for example, saying something could be risky. The person may no longer be in your life at all. Or you may be truly afraid of what he or she might say or do in return, and you need more time or therapy to work on finding the courage.

Q.

How does exercise battle the blues?

A.

It releases into your body endorphins, natural chemical messengers that make you feel better, mentally and physically. It also increases metabolism to get your body humming along smoothly. Finally, it just plain makes you feel good about yourself because you know you've got the self-discipline to follow through on a plan.

The important thing is that you do SOMETHING, even without direct confrontation. You can write an unmailed letter, then forgive this person.

One friend, Lila, prayed for her ex-husband to one day find enough inner peace to know how to treat a woman with love. This helped her get over her resentment when nothing else would.

For someone currently in your life who is hurting you, see the section on Destructive Relationships. You'll need to learn to detach yourself from the situation. To help with the resentments, make the decision to take better care of yourself.

Mary told me the story of how much she used to work on pleasing her mother- and sisters-in-law. Sadly, they put down everything she said or did. It took Mary 20 years, but she finally detached from them in order to let go of her resentment. And what happened? Within a year, they were coming to her for friendship!

"The fact that they suddenly loved me didn't really matter anymore," Mary told me. "It was a nice gift from my higher power for having learned to value myself better, but that wasn't my goal. It might have been my goal 10 years ago. What mattered was that I could feel like a whole person whether they thought I was or not, and that their rejections actually stopped hurting."

---

7) SAY "NO" TO GOSSIP

Few things are more damaging to your integrity and power than gossip. Unless you have to warn someone of an actual danger posed by another person, there is seldom a time when gossip is good for anyone.

Rarely do we gossip out of a true desire to hurt someone else. Usually, we do so in order to create a sense of drama in our lives when we feel bored. We gossip to give ourselves something to talk about when we have little else to say, or in order to create a bond between ourselves and a new friend. But instead of accomplishing any of those things in a meaningful or healthy way, gossip only serves to harm the reputation and perhaps the life of the person you're gossiping about.

In this world, reputation means a lot, and to make someone else doubt a person's character, ethics or competence can have terrible consequences for the person and even his/her family. And ironically, something else gossip does is to ultimately ruin *your* reputation and integrity.

In addition, it gives you a false sense that there is something exciting and stimulating going on in your life, when actually you're wasting time on something that requires no creativity, motivation or effort.

How can I keep depression from affecting my daughter?

The two main sources of a child's mental health are the parents' relationship and mother's stability. With this in mind, try the following:

● Set aside an hour a day for yourself. First, take your blues-fighting herbs and vitamins. Next, indulge yourself in a workout. Finally, take a mineral bath with a loofah scrub.

● Attend a weekly support group such as ACOA, CODA or Al-Anon, where you can turn anger into positive energy.

● Plan activities for your kids to keep them involved and connected to a community.

● Schedule time daily to really give in to your depression. Then, you'll be better able to let it go the rest of the day.

● To keep yourself from snapping at your child, give YOURSELF time-outs when you start to feel annoyed. When you rejoin them, remind yourself of your strength, light and love.

● Try not to burden your child with your problems. Play the role of calm mom and you may become one.

8) TAKE CARE OF YOURSELF

The last step toward self-empowerment is to make YOU and your needs a priority. This includes taking care of your mind, your body and your inner self or soul.

TAKE CARE OF YOUR MIND

- Spend time in libraries or bookstores and give yourself the gift of reading books or magazines that stimulate your mind and make you a more interesting person.

- Start a group with friends with similar interests and ideas.

- Take the supplements we suggest in this book. Many of them will improve your thinking and memory.

- Meditate. Find a quiet area where you won't be disturbed. Relax your muscles, systematically, from head to toe. Don't judge what you're feeling or get annoyed at distractions – just let them "flow through you." Repeat in your mind a sound, word or phrase (called a mantra), or fix your eyes on an object. Focus on the mantra or object instead of on your normal thoughts.

- Every once in a while, get silly, go out for ice cream or go to a funny movie. Everybody needs a recharge now and then.

TAKE CARE OF YOUR BODY

You need to pamper your body from time to time, not only to boost your mood, but also to release toxins and impurities and to improve blood circulation. Here are some ideas:

- Try facials using aromatherapeutic (healing scents, available from health food stores) scrubs and moisturizers.

- Briskly massage your scalp when shampooing.

- Take a mineral salt bath by candlelight, with music in the background.

- Scrub with an invigorating body brush. Use a softer brush around your collarbones and temples. This stimulates the lymphatic and circulatory systems.

- Rub on aromatherapeutic body oils, especially on your stomach and chest.

- Dress well in a style that shows off your personality. It's better to own three outfits that are YOU than six that don't do a thing for you.

- Learn about nutrition and preventive medicine.

TAKE CARE OF YOUR SOUL

- Pursue a spiritual path. See the section on creating spirituality in your life.

- Fill your home with music that lifts the spirit, heals, and makes you feel good.

- Don't push yourself to account for every moment, and check off every task on your "To Do" list. Learn to enjoy the beauty of the world around you, whether it's the joy of being with your children or perhaps a spontaneous night of romance with your husband.

- Perform acts of loving kindness for those in your life whenever possible – not in order to receive anything in return, but simply as an expression of your inner light.

2. "YOU'RE OK, I'M NOTHING"

LOW SELF-ESTEEM:
Edith Bunker in
All in the Family

Low self-esteem can keep you feeling blue, even when everything else in your life is going well.

WHAT IS SELF-ESTEEM?

1. Feeling good about yourself

2. Liking yourself (You'd be surprised how many women don't.)

3. The way you define and judge yourself

WHERE DOES SELF-ESTEEM COME FROM?

> **It's formed by the way our parents treated us as children.**

● Did your parents tend to focus on your good qualities, praise you for them, and give you the chance to do well?

● Did they show you they loved you no matter what?

● Did they criticize things you couldn't change, like your hair, body, personality, taste in clothes?

● Did they seem really happy to spend time with you?

● Did they enjoy learning about your feelings?

● Did they tell you it was okay to take certain risks (such as trying out for the lead role in a play) and then support you?

● When your mother or father was depressed or angry, did they remind you that it wasn't because of you?

● Did they tell you how happy they were that you were a girl, and that you were perfect and wonderful?

Greta, an attractive woman from Miami, FL, told me: "When I was in high school, there was a girl in math class, Jennifer, who was just as homely as I was then. But she was always smiling this big, beautiful smile and her eyes seemed to glow with self-esteem. This actually made her look pretty.

"I couldn't understand her secret. I would try to fake her smile, but I couldn't keep it up. Then, a few years later, while looking through an old photo album, the answer hit me. My parents had hardly any pictures of me, and they had dozens of my sister and brother. My siblings were both attractive kids and I wasn't. My parents gave me less attention, took less pictures, and didn't make comments like, 'Oh, what a beautiful girl you are.'

"But Jennifer's mother treated her like the most beautiful and special girl who graced her parents' lives. The thing was that my parents never said anything bad about my looks. It was what they DIDN'T do or say. And now, when other people tell me how beautiful I am, even when my parents tell me, it doesn't sink in. Inside, I'm always that homely teenager."

> Self-esteem is also dictated by what society and culture expects of girls and women.

● Were you taught that it's okay for a girl to appear intelligent and opinionated?

● Were you taught that your personal success and achievements were as important as those of your brother or other boys?

● Were you taught that it's okay to be complimented or recognized for outstanding achievements, and that it doesn't make you appear arrogant or snobby to do well? Or were you taught that even when you're smart, you should play dumb?

Alicia, a nurse, was always getting praise from doctors, patients and administrators for her outstanding job performance – and always apologizing to co-workers about it. If someone complimented her, she was always quick to dismiss the compliment and put herself down. Her earliest memory of feeling guilty for success was when she was 13 years old and in the seventh grade: "I was new at the school and was nominated to be student council president. To make things more scary, I found out that my opponent was the most popular boy in school. I wanted to win, if not for any other reason than not to suffer the embarrassment of losing. So I wrote a brilliant speech for our school debate that I knew would win votes.

"But when I showed the speech to our science teacher, Mr. Kands, he was worried. He said that Michael's speech was not nearly as good, and that Michael could end up looking like a fool. So I walked out of class having to feel guilty that my speech was superior to Michael's.

"Then I did something I still can't believe. I wrote a speech for Michael. I have to admit I didn't write it quite as well as mine, and I won the election, but that entire year I felt I had to apologize for winning."

> **Self-esteem also comes from labels you were given while growing up.**

● Were you called klutzy or graceful, annoying or sweet, or intelligent or slow?

● Did other kids make fun of your lack of athletic abilities and frailty, or were you called a female jock?

● When you first started dressing to attract boys, did your father think you looked trashy, or pretty and elegant?

● Did your first boss call you bright or spacey?

People get mislabeled, people change...but labels you get stuck with during adolescence can stay with you for the rest of your life.

HOW TO IMPROVE YOUR SELF-ESTEEM

IMPROVED SELF-ESTEEM:
Ally McBeal is learning to assert herself

You can never completely escape the blues until you've taken a good, hard, honest look at yourself and taken active, strong measures to develop your self-esteem.

That's because self-esteem is the foundation from which almost all else develops...your health, personality, reactions, resentments, guilt and sense of power. Almost magically, once your self-esteem improves, circumstances in your life that you always considered totally outside your control may improve as well.

To begin, find yourself a notebook, a good pen and at least two uninterrupted hours of peace and quiet.

STEP 1:

Make a list of all your positive qualities and talents. These can include qualities that relate to your personality (how outgoing, charming, warm, funny and friendly you are); your ability to express honest feelings to others (feelings of love, anger, needs); your competence at work and home; your ability to keep healthy, relationships, your spirituality, your personal values and beliefs; your physical traits; your intelligence, education, etc.

When you have completed the list (and don't be modest!), read it over and feel good!

Are you comfortable with your strengths, or do you find that when people compliment you, you dismiss what they say because you don't think it's true? Do you feel they're just saying it to make you feel better?

Imagine that someone is paying you a compliment right now. Practice saying out loud: "I appreciate what you just said," or "Thank you, your compliment means a lot."

Whatever you do, don't let yourself roll your eyes or put yourself down when you're told that you're special. Think about it for a moment. When you do that, you're actually insulting the other person!

REMEMBER:

True humility comes from knowing your strengths as well as your weaknesses. Recognize that any talents you possess are gifts from a higher power for your good and the good of others. Remember – feeling good about yourself has nothing to do with arrogance!

In truth, people who go out of their way to put themselves down are not showing real modesty at all. What they're doing is fishing for more compliments to fuel their need to feel superior.

STEP 2:

Write a positive statement or affirmation that you can feel comfortable saying each morning and evening. The affirmation should state your good qualities that you value the most. Example: I am a loving, creative and competent woman.

STEP 3:

Make a list of all your negative qualities. You must be totally and fearlessly honest with yourself, or this won't work. There is no need to feel shame while doing this. You can be flawed and still be a wonderful person. Do you set boundaries with other people? This is often a problem for women. Are you unhappy with your body? Write that down, too.

Here is Jacqui's wish list:

❀ I will never fight with my husband.

❀ I will learn to express my needs in a direct, adult manner.

❀ I will become the prettiest mom in the PTA.

❀ I will set limits with family and friends.

❀ I will exercise an hour every day.

STEP 4:

Make another list. On it, write down the qualities you always wished you had...those qualities you've felt you absolutely needed to feel good about yourself.

This is a very significant list because it contains ideas about who you think YOU MUST BE for people to think well of you. This quest for perfection probably began when you were quite young, picked up in messages from your parents. Either that or you took on the need to be perfect because you thought it would please your parents. Look at Jacqui's list for suggestions (Page 40).

There's nothing realistic or constructive about these ideas. In fact, they might be quite destructive. Many women write down that they want to be an all-giving, selfless person. This is absurd! It's not only totally impossible, it's also emotionally and physically harmful.

STEP 5:

The moment of truth! It's no coincidence that every meeting of Alcoholics Anonymous ends with this thoughtful, meaningful prayer:

> *God, grant me the serenity to accept*
> *those things I cannot change; the*
> *courage to change those things I can,*
> *and the wisdom to know the difference.*

Very slowly, go through list #3 (weaknesses) and #4 (wish list) to find the things you can't change or flat-out aren't likely to happen. Also include those things that, deep down, you have to admit you don't really want to change.

For example, many women talk about wanting a better figure. But faced with how much they're willing to sacrifice in terms of time and effort to exercise and eat well, they realize they don't want it all that much!

Others may think they want to be seen as assertive and strong by others. But when faced with that possibility, they realize they don't want to give up being considered selfless.

If the reality of a change is too far-off or too scary, you don't have to try it now. Just keep it in mind.

Now cross all of these items off lists 3 and 4.

Make a final list of the items that are left. These are what you DO have the courage and strength to change. These are the goals you are ready to go for.

STEP 6:

Add another line to the affirmation you started in Step 2. Include those new qualities you are now seeking.

Say the complete affirmation every morning and evening.

> **Here's part of Jacqui's affirmation:**
>
> I will express my needs in a direct, adult manner, establishing boundaries and letting go of my need to criticize.

STEP 7:

You now know what your weaknesses are. Now, put your feet up, close your eyes, and think on this:

You are a wonderful person, deserving of love and forgiveness. Can you forgive yourself for the mistakes you made years ago? Can you love yourself, not despite your weaknesses, but BECAUSE of them?

Your weaknesses show that you are human and that you don't need to be perfect in order to be valued. In fact, when you are loved by yourself or others, weaknesses can be seen as endearing, as part of what makes you special. Promise yourself that you will hold yourself with dignity, accept compliments warmly, and keep a sense of humor about yourself. You will accept who you are, with all your limitations.

Interestingly, it often happens that what seems like a weakness is, in fact, a strength or positive choice.

Karen G. wasn't satisfied with the dinners she served her family. She wanted to be like those old-time mothers who fed their families elaborate meals every night. But when she thought about this "failing"of hers, she realized that it wasn't because she was a bad cook, or that she couldn't get organized. It was because she valued spending time with her children more than anything else.

As a working mom, Karen knew her time was limited. Deep down, she understood it was far better to give her family her love and time than to spend hours in the kitchen.

Q.

Can depression be cured?

A.

Through a combination of social, nutritional, psychological and drug therapy, it can be tamed.

But depression is what is called a "relapsing condition," which means that even after you feel better, you should go back every two months or so to repeat the activity that helped you overcome it.

The key is to channel the blues into creative activities — which many artists and writers have done successfully.

In the meantime, maintain a healthy lifestyle. This includes exercise, nutrition, massage and repeating positive statements to yourself, called "affirmations."

If the depression is serious, ask a doctor about the prescription drugs that are available, such as Prozac. Some people have had good luck taking the herbal remedy, St. John's Wort.

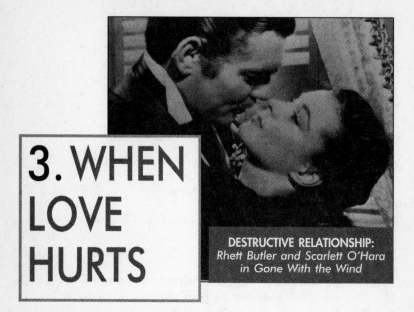

3. WHEN LOVE HURTS

DESTRUCTIVE RELATIONSHIP:
*Rhett Butler and Scarlett O'Hara
in Gone With the Wind*

If you suffer from the blues, examine your relationship with your husband or partner because it will affect:

- ♥ Your self-esteem
- ♥ Your sense of purpose and your hopes
- ♥ Your ability to enjoy life
- ♥ The way you see yourself
- ♥ Your potential, personally and at work
- ♥ Your children and what they will expect of THEIR relationships

Some experts tell you that you should be able to maintain self-esteem on your own – no matter how well or how badly your partner treats you.

But the truth is that women have more of a need to nurture, to relate to others and to be intimate. While some of this is taught to us by society (see *You Can't Please Everyone* in chapter one), to an extent it is a naturally healthy part of a woman's emotional makeup.

Men often have to work at intimacy for a lifetime before they can develop this quality. So if you're being treated in a way that constantly hurts your dignity or self-respect, you're probably experiencing a "wounding of your heart" and a lack of belief in yourself.

Some women, incorrectly, consider the healthy, sensitive part of them that wants a caring, sharing relationship to be immature, weak or overly emotional. But with a possibly abusive partner on one side and a critical society on the other side, it's easy not to know what to think or how to see yourself!

THERE ARE MANY REASONS WHY A RELATIONSHIP

MIGHT BE DESTRUCTIVE:

1. The foundation is bad. Your partner may have emotional or psychological problems that go back to his childhood – and that's something totally out of your control. He may have been abused in some way or lacked a strong (and loving) male role model.

Maybe you married for the wrong reasons. Perhaps because of pregnancy, the desire for a quick escape from an unhappy home life, or because your own low self-esteem allowed you to be attracted to someone abusive.

You may simply be two very different people with different values and interests. Although both of you might be wonderful people with a lot to offer, you may have nothing in common and get no pleasure from each other.

Kathy from Minnesota wrote me: "I married at an early age, and my parents were against the marriage. They could see his faults and knew the effect they would have on me. Not only that, they could see we were on two different planes.

"As my father was walking me down the aisle to take my wedding vows, he whispered in my ear, 'I don't care about losing the money on the wedding. Don't go through with this.'

"'Why?' I asked him.

"'Because,' my father answered, 'he doesn't love Shakespeare and you do.'

"Those were my father's last words to me before I got married. It took me three years before I understood what he meant. At first, it didn't matter to me that I loved to read and talk about deep things and my husband didn't. All I cared about was that he loved me and wanted me.

"But as time went on, I discovered we had nothing in common. His interests, like watching wrestling, annoyed me. My interests bored him. We stopped having things to talk about and began to argue all the time. The day before I had the courage to leave him, I realized that I had stopped writing poetry, stopped doing anything cultural, given up going dancing, stopped attending college. In short, I had given up the best parts of me."

2. You have grown apart. The foundation may have been good at the start, but things have changed. Or the stresses of life and outside circumstances have brought out emotions, reactions and personality changes that put you at odds with each other.

Kathy later told me: "I started going to a non-denominational house of worship where I learned about a higher power, meditation and spirituality. I come home full of insights about life, myself and my marriage, and I want to share them with my husband. He's not the least bit interested.

"What bothers me even more is his anger. He belittles my new philosophies every chance he can. It's almost like the better I feel, the worse he decides to feel.

"Everything has started to decline in our marriage. It's gotten to the point where I'll have to give up my new life, and I don't want to do that, or give up my marriage, and I don't want to do that, either."

What's the best thing to do if I wake up depressed?

Above all, get out of bed.

Get up, exercise, get going, make a plan. If you can, wake up a little early and do something nice for yourself before anyone else gets up, like taking a walk or a bath. That way you won't feel as harried when everyone starts to make demands on you.

WHAT TO DO ABOUT A DESTRUCTIVE RELATIONSHIP

1) UNDERSTAND YOUR PARTNER'S BEHAVIOR AND INTENTIONS

- ♥ He may want to control you by keeping you dependent on his approval and by lowering your self-esteem.

- ♥ He may blame you for things that have nothing to do with you.

- ♥ He may focus anger on you that he feels toward other people he fears (his mother, father, boss, etc.).

48

- ♥ He may get you to blame yourself for the problems in the relationship.

- ♥ He may think of you as someone who only exists to make him happy and to cater to his needs.

- ♥ He may have no idea of emotional and spiritual intimacy with a woman because he always needs to feel in control.

- ♥ He may only be able to feel powerful by making you powerless.

2) SEPARATE YOURSELF FROM THE ABUSE

- ♥ Realize that you're not responsible for his emotional health. You can't fix him.

- ♥ Stop any enabling behavior like paying gambling debts, covering up his drinking problem, etc.

- ♥ Plan more time by yourself or with friends, away from your partner.

- ♥ Develop a support system that will give you a sense of family and esteem. This could be a close group of friends or an actual support group.

- ♥ Start doing things that you used to enjoy, but haven't done because of this relationship (such as listening to music, writing poetry, going bike-riding or to the movies).

- ♥ Don't yell or get overly emotional when you're together. When he says something abusive aimed at turning you into someone you're not, STEP AWAY FROM THE COMMENT. Don't let what he says enter you and change you. Stay cool, confident and strong. In other words, don't give up your power to him.

♥ Release your feelings of rage when you're away from him. Keep a journal of your feelings, the situation and your responses. This will help to reinforce your detachment and will let you see your progress in handling him.

♥ Never let him question your right to your feelings. They are real and they are yours.

♥ Respond to insults carefully so that you remain powerful and detached. Remember that his insults are a reflection of HIM, not of you.

♥ When your partner asks you to do something that doesn't feel right, learn to calmly say, "No."

♥ Don't become mean or vindictive like him. A person's greatest victory is to make you like him!

Try using one of the following comebacks when he's critical:

1) "Let me clarify what you just said. You said...? Is this exactly what you meant?"

2) "You're not making sense now. Let's talk later." (Then walk away).

3) "It's hard for me to hear this now. Let's try later!" (Then walk away).

4) Change the subject. Ask an unrelated question or make an unrelated statement. This tells him that what he is saying is of no importance to you, and that takes away his power.

DESTRUCTIVE RELATIONSHIPS

> A friend, Jackie, once said, "If my husband told me I was green and from the planet Mars, would I get enraged and lose my self-esteem? No! Because I know that's not true. So why should I ever let any other ridiculous comment bother me?"

3) HOW TO BUILD A HEALTHY RELATIONSHIP

The goal of any good relationship is "interdependence."

This is a state where each of you agrees to love, nurture, respect and support the other toward common life goals. But if your relationship is abusive, you must first gain a sense of independence and detachment.

Always be in tune with your own needs (intellectual, emotional, spiritual, physical) and actively seek them. Be firm and calm when stating them to your partner.

When you need to express anger or hurt to your partner, cool down first by writing in your journal and talking to someone about it. When you do talk to him, focus on your feelings and reactions to the situation, not on how bad or weak he is. If you focus on your partner's weakness, he will get defensive and angry, and you will make no progress.

If your partner genuinely makes up for harming you, don't stay resentful. Let yourself experience fun and romance.

Remember to guard the limits and boundaries we talked about earlier. If they're being crossed, something is wrong.

If you find yourself doing more than your fair share of something that is the responsibility of you both, DON'T! That will ultimately make both of you resentful. And it will keep him from growing up and appreciating a healthy relationship.

51

4. IT'S NOT EASY BEING SUPERWOMAN

People pleasing isn't just something that comes from inside you. It's the exhausting reality of being a woman today.

DO ANY OF THESE SOUND FAMILIAR?

✳ "If I take care of all my work and the house, the kids get out of control and I feel like a terrible mother. But if I give my children my energy and attention, everything else falls apart."

✳ "The only way to get everything done, and to take care of everyone in the family, is to work every night until midnight. If I do that, my husband complains I'm not spending time with him. But if I stop everything to be with him, he complains about the house."

Dinnertime for most women can be the most stressful time of the day.

If you're a homemaker, it can be particularly frustrating because you and your husband have such different needs.

52

Women who have been home all day look forward to their husband coming home all afternoon.

It's a time for renewing your intimacy, having stimulating conversation and sharing some of the responsibilities of the home.

Men, however, tend to see coming home and having dinner very differently. They want private time. Often, they'll head straight for a quiet room to wind down.

If you're a working wife and mother, dinnertime is when you're expected to perform miracles. It's easy to see why the task of juggling home, career and family is called the "Superwoman Syndrome."

While all the unfinished business from the workday is still floating in your head, you're supposed to calm everyone else's nerves, deal

53

with everyone else's problems, and turn the home from chaos into order.

All that and you're still expected to be cheerful! Even in the very best circumstances, the exhaustion of life can pull down your spirits. Car pools, softball games, doctor appointments, birthday parties, career and evening classes, all with no letup, can sometimes make the best life seem stale and joyless.

Q.

Is psychotherapy right for me?

Sometimes you just can't go it alone. You need an objective person to give you the understanding and the determination to change.

A therapist can help you feel the love you need for your self-esteem. She can affirm your worth and "okayness" while pointing out hurtful patterns and giving you the "push" you need to change.

Here's how to choose a therapist:

● First, find someone with the right expertise. There are therapists who specialize in eating disorders, depression, divorce, etc.

● Then, check out the person's style of therapy. Some are supportive and offer counseling and advice; some give a kind of tough love; while still others bring about true personality change through analysis and interpretations of your past.

● Finally, try to find someone whose values are close to your own.

HOW TO GET CONTROL OF YOUR HOME LIFE

If you've got the blues because you're overworked, unappreciated and overtired, you CAN do something about it. Although there are no techniques that will completely take the stress out of taking care of a job, house and family, you can gain a better sense of order and control, and with it, a lot more happiness.

CHILDREN

You may spend hours worrying that you're not an attentive enough mother. Because you're overtired and distracted by work or other endeavors, you're not always able to concentrate on your children's self-esteem or emotional development. If you have young children, you probably have times when you find yourself wondering,  "Who's in control here, because it doesn't seem to be me!"

HERE'S A SIMPLE PROGRAM THAT WILL BOOST YOUR CHILD'S SELF-ESTEEM AND SELF-DISCIPLINE:

STEP 1:

Sit down (preferably with your husband) and make a list of your child's strengths and talents. Include things about his or her character that are positive and a link to building ethics and values.

HERE'S WHAT TO DO:

> **EXAMPLE:**
> **Mindy's Strengths and Talents: (Mindy is age 5)**
> 1) She is kind to people who are sad or troubled. Likes to defend the underdog
> 2) Athletic and physically strong
> 3) Funny and entertaining
> 4) Excellent memory
> 5) Loves to be read to

✳ Look for every opportunity to praise your child for doing any of these things. Often we only praise our child when he or she does something exceptional or new. But there are already lots of wonderful things about your child that you can capitalize on to build self-esteem.

✳ You must praise your child frequently. He or she will get used to hearing praise and appreciation, and work even harder not to lose that great feeling. Your child will see himself/herself as a good person.

✳ A great time to give praise is when you tuck your child in at night. Be specific about all the positive things he or she did during the day. Ask them to mention some positive activities, especially acts of kindness, and then tell them how well they have done.

✳ Create more opportunities for your child to develop his or her talents and interests. This should include group activities (such as after-school classes and teams), parent/child activities to create a life-long bond, and individual activities to build resourcefulness and self-discipline. Turn off the TV!

✳ Create family rituals and family activities that promote ethics and values.

✳ Organize an after-school schedule. This list should include: homework time, bath time, bedtime rituals, and an interesting choice of projects and hobbies to build character or intelligence. Make sure bedtime is about the same every night (especially school nights).

✳ Keep a list of your children's responsibilities at home. These chores should always include cleaning their room (even at age four they can do at least a little) and getting ready for school and bed on time. Privileges (such as watching a movie or occasional TV) should depend on following through on all responsibilities.

REMEMBER:

If you keep your child busy enough with positive things to do, he or she won't have time to become bored or badly behaved.

STEP 2:

Make a list of all your child's negative or bothersome behaviors. These should include everything that you put energy into worrying about or reacting to.

EXAMPLE: Mindy's Negative Behaviors
1) Loud voice and talks too much
2) Sometimes disrespectful
3) Doesn't clean room, always a mess

Study your list carefully and cross out any problem that is NOT in your child's control, but simply part of his or her temperament.

In Mindy's example, this would be her loud voice. Voice and its intensity are qualities we're born with and, to a great extent, they're not within our control. Also cross out anything that is part of what normally goes on at your child's age, as well as anything that may turn into a good quality if shaped correctly. For Mindy, her talking too much could become a professional asset.

REMEMBER:

From now on, don't waste your time or energy worrying about anything that's crossed off your list.

Q.
When it comes to depression, can I "think myself well?"

A.
I believe in the saying, "Fake it till you make it." In other words, if you start to smile and act happy (within reason), you will actually create those pathways for the natural blues-fighting body chemicals to flow through. And you'll feel better.

Think about it. Not only could you never change those things anyway, but mentioning them to children ends up hurting their feelings and damaging their self-esteem. Children are particularly sensitive to criticisms about things they know they can't help. It feels to them like you're attacking their inner selves – and that hurts on a pretty deep level. Then, when you want to reprimand them for something they CAN change, they're already angry or defensive and won't listen.

STEP 3:

In regard to the negative behaviors that are still left on your list, decide upon the two or three problems that you want to begin to work on. Ask yourself what positive qualities could replace your child's negative qualities, since those are what you want to create. In Mindy's case, for example, her mother wanted Mindy to become respectful and organized.

Call a family meeting. Announce that there's a new sheriff in town, and that it's you (and your husband). Explain that from now on, your child's problem behaviors are his or her problems and that he or she will suffer the consequences from them. They are not your problems. Your child is responsible for his or her own actions.

Explain the consequences of bad behavior. These should depend on the child's age and on the nature (and seriousness) of the offense.

For young children, "time-outs" (sending them away from the "action" for a short, specific period of time) can work well, along with taking away privileges such as playtime or television.

Then focus on the positive things. Tell your child that you know that he is respectful and organized, that you will help in developing these qualities even more, and that from now on, you expect them on a day-by-day basis. If necessary, make a star chart on which you give stars each day for good behavior.

For the next three weeks, make a point not to criticize your child at all. Instead, concentrate on changing the two or three behaviors you pinpointed above by "punishing" negative behaviors (stick to the consequences you explained) and praising positive behaviors. See what happens.

HOME

Make a list of all your responsibilities and daily/monthly tasks. Write down next to each one if it is something that can be done by someone else (such as your husband or an older child), something that you don't really need to do at all, or something that can be organized better.

Call a family meeting. Firmly state that you are not supermom. You are not willing to sacrifice your health or sanity any longer! Ask your husband and/or children to take on certain tasks. You can present them with choices as to what they want to do. If you feel pretty sure that they can perform these tasks, let go of your worries about them afterward.

Your family may have a hard time adjusting at first. But if you keep looking over their shoulders and monitoring how they're doing a job, you might as well do it yourself!

Buy or make a giant family calendar. Figure out how you can organize certain tasks (such as paying bills) so that they're not always on your mind. Plan them out on your calendar.

For paying the bills, plan two nights a month when that's all you do. Don't worry about them on any other night. Keep all personal and family activities on the calendar so you don't have to keep commitments and dates in your head.

Mark two drawers your "To Do" drawers. One should be for priority things that must be done right away. The other should be for things that can build up for a few weeks. Keep a "To Do" list on you at all times.

REMEMBER:

What's most draining is not the work, but worrying about the work, especially if there are a million details you're afraid you'll forget. So keep everything listed and organized.

When you leave work every day, make a "To Do" list of what

was left undone. Why? Many women tell me that their biggest problem at home is that they can't stop worrying about work. As a result, they can't concentrate fully on their children or feel romantic with their husbands. They end up feeling guilty and depressed about this, but they can't stop.

A "To Do" list at the close of each workday will help you make the mental shift back home. If you know that all your remaining work is listed and organized for your return to work the next day, you can have peace of mind and concentrate on the family. When you're able to give your family your complete attention, it's amazing how much more effectively everything will run.

Q.

Is there a connection between body image and depression?

A.

Yes. Women's feelings about their attractiveness, which in our culture means thinness, are wrapped up with their self-worth.

Many women think that they're fatter than they are. When asked to trace their body shapes on a big piece of paper and then stand in front of it, nine times out of 10, women find they're a good deal thinner than they think they are. But even this exercise doesn't help them change the way they think.

There's nothing wrong with wanting to look your best. But it can get out of hand.

One woman I know in her mid-30s, Cecile, is so self-conscious about her looks that she won't accept any dates. Now shouldn't the fact that she's TURNING DOWN dates convince her that she's by no means unattractive? Sadly, her obsessive concern about her weight kept her from dealing with anything else in her life.

5. DON'T GET EVEN, GET MAD!

HOLDING BACK ANGER: *Kitty Montgomery in Dharma & Greg*

One of the major causes of women's blues is stuffing down all that anger.

Anger is a natural, legitimate emotion. We are all entitled to feel anger and to express it appropriately. Left unexpressed, anger can poison your body and your mind. It can cause depression, fatigue, cancer, anxiety and resentment that control your life.

But as children, many women lost the ability to express anger – and even to know when they feel it. Why? It varies from woman to woman. Some were taught as toddlers that anger and independence were punishable. They became ashamed and afraid about anger.

Some saw as young children that expressing anger hurt their mother or father's feelings. These children were made to feel that it was their job to look after the emotional balance and self-esteem of their parents.

Thus, anger is squelched, and the child thinks, "I can't be angry at my parent. I should feel sorry for her/him." Once grown up, the woman who was "parent-icized" earlier will talk herself out of her anger. She will tell herself the offending party should only get her sympathy, never her anger.

For other women, expressing anger as a child may have been met with rejection. The parents may have withheld love, affection and support. In these cases, the girl grows up fearing that anger will cause those she loves to abandon her.

Just like people pleasing, society encourages women not to feel anger.

My friend Kelly told me, "My boss treats me like trash and I lie awake all night, night after night, imagining what it would be like to tell him off. But I've seen how he reacts to women when they get angry. He just mutters that they're "on the rag" or a bitch. I'm afraid that expressing my anger will just make him laugh, or give him ammunition against me."

Kelly's experience is typical. Things at the workplace are supposed to be non-sexist in today's world, but old stereotypes persist. Men who appear strong (even aggressive) and who express their feelings bluntly and directly are seen as leaders. Their expressions of anger are seen as reasonable, and a sign of strength and conviction.

Women who are equally forthright and direct are often seen, condescendingly, as overpowering, cold and unbalanced.

How does the media teach women to hold back their anger?

The role models for women in books and movies mainly show the ideal woman as handling anger in one of the following three ways:

1) THE MARTYR

This is a woman like Melanie Wilkes in *Gone With the Wind*. Even when Melanie knew that Scarlett was plotting to steal her husband and would scorn her every chance she could, Melanie always gracefully and nobly forgave her. On her deathbed, Melanie even handed her husband over to Scarlett.

2) THE GOOD GIRL

This is portrayed beautifully by the character of *Cinderella*, one of the first stories a little girl learns. Instead of complaining and standing up for her rights, Cinderella represses her anger at the ugly stepsisters, scrubs the floor and sits politely in the corner. At the end, she is rewarded for being so good by winning the hand of the prince.

HE could rescue her, but SHE couldn't rescue herself.

In *The Wizard of Oz*, Dorothy bravely tries to show anger at her nasty neighbor when she comes to take her dog Toto away. But Dorothy's Aunt Em doesn't support her, and Dorothy is left with no choice but to run away.

In her dream, Dorothy learns to be independent and strong. But when the dream is over, she gives her power back to her aunt and uncle by dutifully and sweetly acknowledging: "There's no place like home." In other words, books and movies tell us that anger can be expressed by good girls only in a dream.

3) PASSIVE/AGGRESSIVE

This is portrayed by the wives in the sitcoms of the '50s and '60s. Lucy Ricardo, played by Lucille Ball in *I Love Lucy*,

64

is a perfect example. Rather than making their wants and anger clear to their husbands, these women created amusing situations to teach their husbands a lesson — while they stood by innocently.

Unlike the spiritual martyr and the good girl, this type of "passive-aggressive" woman DOES get what she wants. But it's through manipulation and games, never through a direct, healthy expression of honest feeling.

DO YOU HOLD BACK ANGER?

● Do you dread seeing certain people in your life because of the way they've treated you? Have you let your anger build up so that when you're with them, you have knots in your stomach and feel withdrawn and depressed?

● Do you feel that you're "walking on eggshells" at home, always having to smooth over the feelings of your husband?

● Do you tend to feel hurt rather than angry?

● When you're angry at someone, do you give them the silent treatment? Then, when that person asks you what's wrong, do you say, "Nothing"?

● When you're angry at someone, do you somehow forget to do things for that person, like giving cards or phoning?

● Do you tend to "explain away" people's rudeness?

● Do you feel sorry for people who have hurt you?

● Are you afraid that if you ever did let your anger out toward someone, years of resentment would be unleashed and you would lose control of your emotions?

● Are you afraid that if you expressed your anger toward someone in a calm, appropriate way, he or she would reject you?

● Do you have many accidents?

HOW TO HEAL HELD-BACK ANGER

MAKE THE DECISION TO HEAL

How? By giving yourself permission to experience the feeling of anger.

Remember that hurt, excessive guilt, resentment, perfectionism, shame, depression and emotional numbness may ALL be signs of hidden anger — anger that you're afraid to acknowledge.

For example, children who suffer from severe anxiety when they must separate from a parent (such as when going to school) may actually have anger toward that parent that they feel too guilty to express.

LEARN THE REASONS FOR YOUR ANGER

Are there people in your past or present who have hurt you, and whom you continue to excuse? Are you angry at yourself because you let yourself be drawn into self-destructive patterns of behavior or abusive relationships? You may need to go back through your childhood and examine old memories as well as painful patterns in your life.

REFRAME YOUR HURT AND PAIN INTO ANGER

For a memory that you used to say "hurt you," reframe it by saying aloud to yourself, "This memory angers me."

Feel the anger flow through your body. If you can do this, you will feel – almost immediately – the release of pent-up feelings that were stored inside of you, creating illnesses and depression for years.

RELEASE OLD ANGER

You must fully experience anger in all its intensity before you release it. In a safe space, with a person you trust or by yourself, let out the anger. Replay old scenes, saying aloud with passion what you wished you said years ago.

Hit your bed with a tennis racket, starting with your knees bent, your arms high over your head, then lowering the racket so that it hits the bed squarely in front of you. While doing it, shout, "Ya" in a full voice that comes from deep within your stomach.

FEEL YOUR POWER AND YOUR FEELINGS

Don't make excuses for the people who have harmed you. Don't forgive them until the anger is released. Stay IN the anger – you deserve it. Forgiveness, reconnection and peace can come afterward. But forgiveness can only truly be given once the anger is acknowledged and expressed. Otherwise, it's false.

HEAL CURRENT ANGER

Work through the sections in this book on resentments and self-esteem. Talk with "I" statements that tell people about your feelings, limits and boundaries. Anger usually comes from putting yourself in a situation where you allow someone to take advantage of you. In other words, prevention is your best defense.

6. WHEN YOU FEEL NOTHING

DO ANY OF THESE STATEMENTS APPLY TO YOU?

- I have a hard time trusting people.
- I am especially afraid of men, doctors or people in authority.
- I "space out" a lot.
- I often feel that I'm detached, that I'm just watching myself going through the motions.
- I'm very sensitive to loud noises or loud voices.
- I always need to feel in control.
- I only feel okay when my house is clean and everything is in order.
- I don't like getting too close to people or letting them know how I feel.
- I have a desire to "self-medicate" by using alcohol or drugs.
- I need to do something intense (physically or sexually) to feel anything at all.

These statements are all from women who have gone through childhood trauma. Trauma can take many forms. It can, in the worst cases, be physical or sexual. Or it can take subtle forms, such as emotional abuse, or a lack of love.

Depending on the amount and type of pain you suffered, the amount of support you did or did not receive from at least one constant adult figure in your childhood, and your own temperament and personality, the pain may have gotten to the point where you couldn't stand it.

When that happened, the mind did an amazing thing. It actually pushed the trauma out of your awareness so that you could get on with your life.

There's a problem with this nifty mechanism of repressing painful feelings and memories, however. It makes you numb. True, you don't feel pain, but you can't feel love, enthusiasm, or many other emotions, either.

Trauma and numbing can also be caused by a trauma suffered during adulthood. The loss of a loved one, divorce or a catastrophic experience can create an overload in the mind of painful feeling, making the sufferer, once again, feel nothing.

FIVE STEPS TO FEELING

1) You must open the door not only to the suppressed memories of the original trauma(s), but also to the memory of what it felt like at the age of your experience. Your recollections should ideally combine the images, sounds, smells, tastes, visions and feelings associated with the memory.

If you have trouble remembering or reliving the trauma, use a memory trigger such as old pictures, artwork, dance and movement, bodywork with a massage therapist, or "inner child work" (learning to understand the child inside you) and hypnotherapy with a therapist.

2) Fully experience your anger and painful feelings.

3) Grieve the loss of that part of your life. Part of the numbing comes from not accepting, without even realizing it, what has happened to you. On a deep level, you must recognize the reality and significance of the trauma. Only then will you gain power over it, because when memories remain buried, they still have power over you. Grieving the pain and loss resulting from the trauma gives you control over the trauma and lets real healing begin.

4) Activate your grief so that it becomes constructive instead of destructive. Destructive grief leaves you numb, despairing, disconnected from others and yourself. Constructive grief is passionate. You feel your pain and loss passionately. Then you move passionately to action, planning and moving toward inner strength and the full repair of your emotional wounds.

5) Actively retrain your thinking (this can be done with a therapist) to fully realize the following truths:

* You were not responsible for the trauma.

* You did not deserve the trauma.

* You can trust your feelings and memories.

* It is not your job to meet your parents' emotional needs.

* You have a right to personal boundaries, both physical and emotional.

* You are good and deserve love and respect, even if you're not perfect.

* You can create an emotionally and physically safe environment for you (and your children) to live in.

* You can experience true intimacy with a partner.

7. WHAT TO DO?

BOREDOM:
Maryann
Thorpe
in Cybill

It's sometimes hard to admit you're bored because it seems so childish. But boredom may be hiding something serious or calling your attention to your problems.

WHAT CAN BOREDOM HIDE?

What you think is boredom can actually be a physical condition such as clinical depression, chronic fatigue, a systemic candida infection, food allergies, or one of many other disorders. Boredom can show up in the following ways:

Poor appetite/Apathy/Inability to enjoy anything/Lack of motivation to establish a goal or go after a goal/ Poor concentration/Sluggishness or "not feeling well"

See a doctor if the feeling lasts more than two weeks.

71

WHAT CAUSES BOREDOM?

There are a number of problems, both inside and outside an individual, that can trigger boredom.

* You can't discipline yourself to stick to a goal or difficult task. You go instead for the short-term rewards. As a result, you can't pursue WITH PASSION an interest or personal goal that requires continuous dedication and mental/physical work.

* You've made material things (such as cars, a nice house, clothes) too much of a priority.

* You're unable to "live in the moment," to enjoy what you're doing at the time because you're too busy worrying about something else.

* Due to poor self-esteem or people pleasing, you won't let yourself experience the joy of having fun or putting time into something for yourself.

* You've stopped thinking of yourself as an interesting person with something to offer others.

* You're unconsciously angry at your husband or partner for not being supportive of your specific goals (so you refuse to be excited doing anything else).

* You feel frustrated because you haven't accomplished the things in life you've wanted to, and now you feel that all attempts are futile.

* You're afraid of failure, so you're afraid to try.

HOW TO GO FROM BORED TO PASSIONATE

PASSIONATE:
Roseanne Conner

1) Become proactive, not reactive.

Boredom happens when we let life happen to us, rather than creating our lives in a strategic, energetic way.

2) Act with courage and confidence.

Boredom happens when we're afraid of failing or fearful of being rejected, so we just sit around initiating nothing.

3) Act with playfulness.

Some religions consider what we're doing here in this world as "divine play." It's okay to be a little wacky and spontaneous. Our souls need it.

4) Record in a notebook your life goals and interests.

Under each life goal and interest, make a list of small things or activities that could be done to achieve it. Then, when you're bored, go to your list – and go for it!

8. A FAILURE AT SUCCESS

For a married man, it's pretty simple to decide what's most important in his life. At the top of the list is the job that gives him status and makes sure his family is taken care of. This is followed by his roles as husband and father.

PROBLEMS AT WORK:
Agent Scully in The X-Files

Conflicts can come up if the demands at the office mean that he has to work late or during the weekend. But there's generally not a lot of difference between his own needs and the expectations that society and his family have of him.

For a married woman or mother, on the other hand, the decision on what to put first in her life is often filled with conflict, confusion and guilt. Like many women, you were probably brought up to believe that nothing should be more important as a grown-up than being a wife and mother.

You were probably never presented with female role mod-

74

els who were driven by professional ambition. Later, you may have been given the double message from parents, friends or the media that as a complete woman, you should go after a meaningful career (so long as you still take care of your family and home).

What's more, your life at home may not have been as fulfilling as you expected, and you needed something more. The question of where to direct most of your energies – to your family or work – is emotionally charged.

On one hand, you have been made to believe that if you weren't a supermom you couldn't be a good person. On the other hand, society now insists that you can only be considered worthwhile if you have a good job.

Let's take these issues one at a time:

It's not surprising that the blues can be triggered when your decision to seek success at work brings up deep fears and insecurities.

These include the following:

1) FEAR OF LOSING THE LOVE OF YOUR HUSBAND

Many men openly tell their wives that they want them to be happy and fulfilled professionally. Husbands have told me it was always their original intention that their wife go back to college or work one day, that she have the opportunity to put less time into taking care of the family and more time into her work.

But talk is cheap, and often a man says what he thinks he should say as a caring, modern husband without really examining if he's capable of living up to the reality of it.

The truth is that many men are extremely dependent on

their wives (which often has a lot to do with their relationships with their mothers). They themselves may not be aware of how strongly this dependency affects them until the day comes when the women in their lives put on suits, pick up briefcases and head out to work.

Shaken by the emotion that arises when a man sees his wife become professionally successful, and angry at himself for feeling the fear and dependency he realizes he has, he may react with anger.

You may have borne the brunt of this anger in many different ways. In some couples I've seen, the husband becomes controlling and hostile, sometimes threatening to leave if his wife didn't return to the role of dutiful caretaker.

But in most cases, the husband's anger comes out in a gentler, but still destructive form. He may get angry at unrelated little things, like the fact that dinner's not ready on time (the anger is usually about his not being taken care of well enough).

He may withhold love and intimacy. He may praise other women in his life (such as his mother or sister) who knew how to take care of him better. (That one really hurts, doesn't it?)

2) FEAR OF ANGERING WOMEN IN AUTHORITY

A major obstacle for women in asserting themselves at work and becoming successful stems from the fear that it will make their women bosses angry and jealous.

If this is happening to you, focus on your relationship with your mother – past and present. As a child, she may have beamed with pride when you did well in school, perhaps because your success was a reflection of her.

But now as an adult, when you tell her about your accomplishments or try to have a conversation as equals, she becomes bitter or distant. She may prefer you to remain in the child role, with you coming to her for advice and support when things aren't going well.

A controlling, critical mother who doesn't let her daughter become an adult sets up a reenactment of the mother-daughter relationship with a strong female boss.

Your relationship with a female boss can take various forms:

1) You may be drawn into playing the role of the nice, non-threatening girl who is willing to listen politely and sweetly to all advice given by your boss (in order to keep her from getting angry).

2) You may try to win your boss' love with kindness, compliments and exaggerated humbleness in order to gain her "love."

3) You may rebel against your mother by rebelling against your boss (often in a passive/aggressive way such as forgetting to remind your boss of an appointment).

4) You may try to do the healthy thing and impress your boss by doing a great job. However, this can backfire and cause much grief if your boss has a jealousy problem and doesn't know how to be a mentor. She could react with as much anger as your mother.

Kathryn, a junior high school teacher, told me how things backfired when she tried to win the approval of her boss:

"On my 22nd birthday I started as the new, young teacher at my school. Instantly, I knew that my department head Diane, age 40, hated me. My first day at work, she actually invited everyone in our department by name to lunch except me. At first, I thought her dislike was my imagination, that I was being overly sensitive. I needed her to like me.

"But no matter how nice I was, she looked through me like I wasn't even there. I thought I could win her over by becoming the best teacher possible. But the more my students respected me and the more progress they made, the more hostile and cruel Diane became.

"I started hearing through the grapevine that she talked about me all the time. I couldn't believe that someone as respected and powerful as she was at the school could possibly be jealous of me.

"Then I learned that the week before I started at the school, Diane's husband had left her for a woman about my age. Even worse, our principal told Diane that I would probably be a great success. To her I represented everything that threatened her."

3) INSECURITY ABOUT PLAYING THE ROLE OF THE ADULT PROFESSIONAL

Women were traditionally taught by their parents to act in a charming, feminine and nurturing way. They were taught that it is more important to be liked than respected, to be the peacemaker instead of the trailblazer.

Fathers especially encouraged their daughters to be coquettish, and rewarded lovable and agreeable behavior. Meanwhile, sons were often taught to think independently, to stand on their own and act resourcefully, and most importantly, to stick up for themselves in order to gain respect.

At work, people are rewarded more often for traits that were encouraged in boys than for those encouraged in girls.

The rewards are very different, as well. To be successful at work, a person must be able to occasionally withstand the dislike, anger or jealousy of others while pursuing a goal or task. She must be able to think quickly and clearly, to make decisions, and to put tasks ahead of people.

If the quality you've been most rewarded for is your charm and your self-esteem depends on being liked, you may feel anxious about putting your career goals ahead of your need to be liked. For some women, this can cripple their ability to perform competently. And, sadly, the reward for success, which is status and respect, may feel uncomfortable.

Because Jacqueline was very smart as a child, the other kids rejected her. Enviously, she'd watch the "average" kids who were more popular than she. She learned through imitation that playing down her strengths was the way to win their approval.

As a young woman, Jacqueline was made supervisor of a department of six women. She made a point to tell her employees to think of her as one of them. She told them that they needn't fear her like their previous supervisor (who was now manager).

A week later, her secretary started going through a divorce, and due to emotional problems, came in late to work for a week. Jacqueline didn't say anything about her behavior out of fear of being seen as "the boss."

The other women in the department saw their co-worker coming in late and started doing the same. Things in the department slowly began to get out of control. Jacqueline often had to almost beg some of the women to get their work done on time. But they had stopped taking her seriously, and Jacqueline eventually lost her position.

HOW TO BECOME STRONGER AT WORK

STRONG AT WORK:
Murphy Brown

You have to understand what work is for and not for. Work is NOT a place for being loved, physically desired, taken care of emotionally, or working out emotional problems of the past.

Work is the place for being, hopefully, respected. Respected not because you're a wonderful person, but because you're extremely competent and focused on what you do.

Every time you have to make a decision on what course of action to take at work, such as whether or not to take on a project, ask yourself the following questions:

1) What is the purpose of my decision. Is it to "look good" and get somebody to like me, or is it because it's the right thing to do?

2) Am I acting out of fear of being "punished" or disliked, or am I fully pursuing a goal in an emotionally stable, professional way?

✳ Set limits and boundaries around yourself, very much like the way you do in a relationship. You should not be the dumpster for anyone else's emotional problems, nor the object for locker room talk. Tolerate nothing less than professional behavior. Look crisp and professional every day. Casual or sexy styles of dress create a weaker image.

✳ Avoid talking about personal problems or experiences at work. That's what friends outside of work are for. Remember, you don't want to be loved or pitied at work, simply respected.

✳ If you have a little girl voice, work on deepening it. Consider voice lessons or exercises that enable you to speak from your diaphragm and not your throat.

✳ When talking with coworkers, smile and act positive. Keep conversations focused on work-related tasks. Never get into group gossip or general griping.

✳ Figure out your professional goals. Where do you want to be five years from now?

Q.

What is the cyclical role of depression?

A.

Moods are affected by all kinds of cycles. You may have heard of Seasonal Affective Disorder, a type of blues that primarily strikes light-sensitive Northerners during the dark, winter months. And each life change, whether it's going to college, getting married, menopause, retirement, whatever – involves a sort of mourning for the old ways.

Even during the course of a day, we go through cycles. In the morning, body temperature, metabolism and the adrenal systems are at their lowest levels.

9. PARTY OF ONE

LIVING ALONE:
Susan Keene in Suddenly Susan

Women today are putting off marriage, deciding not to marry at all, or ending their marriages – for all sorts of reasons.

♥ They are trying to finish college, graduate school or a vocational program. This will let them live up to society's new standard for a woman: that she be financially independent, educated and able to support herself.

♥ They are spending more time on "finding themselves." For some this means delving into their pasts through therapy, self-help groups and alternative techniques to gain an understanding of who they really are and how to make themselves whole.

♥ They are less willing to tolerate abuse, unfaithfulness and lack of respect in a marital relationship. Their standards are higher than those of women in previous generations.

As Delores from Boca Raton, FL, told me, "Better to be single and a little lonely, than in a lonely marriage. There's almost nothing worse than being alone when someone else is actually there."

The consequence of setting higher standards for themselves and their spouses before and during marriage is that many women are much stronger and happier when they ARE married. But many more women are now alone and living their 30s, 40s and beyond without a partner or children — sometimes not by choice.

Carole, an artist, explained: "Besides the aspect of not having anyone to share your life with, there are lots of horrible things about being alone that you don't realize unless you go through it.

"When you're not married, you don't have the new family you're supposed to. So all you have are your parents. You end up worrying constantly about something happening to them because then you are REALLY alone.

"And while other women have husbands and children to talk about, it gets old talking to people about your parents or pets. People start thinking you're strange. When you're sick, forget it. There's no one to bring you tea or juice, buy your medicine, drive you to the doctor. Sometimes I'll panic and worry that something terrible will happen to me and no one will know.

"Going out is always a problem. I'm always the lone ranger, and even when people go out of their way to make me feel comfortable, I can't help feeling self-conscious. I'm afraid when I'm out with a couple that the man is going to like me and that his wife is going to get jealous and end our friendship.

"Food gives me the blues because there's no one to cook for. Sometimes I hear a friend complain because of all the shopping and cooking she has to do for her family and I actually get jealous. I'll bet I eat sandwiches for dinner at least six nights a week.

"The worst is holidays and coming home at night. It's a weird feeling, even after being single for five years, to know there's no one waiting up for you, no one to care that you've gotten home safely, no one to ask how your day was. This much freedom as a teenager would have been really exciting. Now, however, it's just depressing."

While single parenthood for women might be the most emotionally and physically draining commitment imaginable, life without children – even while single – is being considered by many women to be the hardest loss to bear.

But Jill R. had a different perspective:

"For me, being single is wonderful. Since no one else is responsible for my happiness, I'm not in a constant state of anger and resentment like many of my married friends. And I have a lot of time to take care of myself.

"What gets me down is other people's reactions to me. If a man is single, couples are quick to invite him out with them, but they're not so quick with a single woman. Head waiters in restaurants look strangely at me if I'm a "party of one" and never give me a good table.

"I either get pity (who wants it?) or the inquisition from relatives. But the more I tell them I'm happy, the more they give me a sympathetic look as if I'm in denial about my depression. But they're the reason I'm depressed!"

LIVING ALONE WITH HAPPINESS

SINGLE & HAPPY:
Oprah Winfrey

Here's how to learn to love and appreciate the benefits of being single.

● Your time is truly your own. You can develop talents, hobbies and interests, and fall in love with these pursuits. You have the power and the time to become an incredible woman and role model for others.

● You have time to dedicate to your health. You can do what other women only dream about! Turn your home into a mini spa. Cook gourmet health meals, make organic vegetable juices, practice aromatherapy and body brushing, do aerobics and stretching exercises.

● You have time to develop your mind. Read, study, go to classes and study groups at night. Become a self-made scholar on a topic you have a passion for.

● Pursue self-expansion. Learn how to meditate and practice yoga or another Oriental art. Radiate light and healing to others. Feel your connection to others through your role as teacher or role model.

● Create strong support systems of friends. Plan vacations and outings.

● Get involved with projects that reflect your convictions and values. Make friends through these projects who have similar philosophies.

● Create an atmosphere at home that is nurturing to your soul.

● Allow yourself to value the love of friends. It is no less valuable than any other love. Society may tell you that you should be depressed without a man. Yet in fact, single women are considered one of the happiest groups.

● If you still feel that you're not complete without a man, know that your best chance for meeting someone who is good for you will be when you can feel happy and confident on your own. You end up conveying something non-verbally that will draw people to you like a magnet.

What foods can I eat to battle the blues?

All-around good nutrition is the key here.

A smoothly functioning body will definitely help.

But in particular, reach for those foods containing the B complex or "nerve vitamins," which include whole grains, organ meats (heart, liver, kidneys), brewer's yeast, wheat germ, dairy products (but don't load up on these), fish, nuts, blackstrap molasses, some beans. Not all vitamins are present in each food, so you'll need a mixture.

Fruit gives you a nice, natural energy lift – without the plunging low you get an hour after eating a candy bar. Adding one cup of coffee in the morning and one around 4 p.m. will lift your mood and energy level without keeping you up.

Limit dairy products, meat, fried foods and white flour. In addition, you may wish to be tested for food allergies and sensitivities, both of which can affect your mood.

10. THE THRILL IS GONE

LACK OF ROMANCE:
Peg and Al Bundy in Married . . . With Children

I first met Sara when she and her husband Ken had been married for 10 years. On the surface, things were going well in their marriage.

"We've gone through a lot together and have gotten to the point where we hardly fight," Sara told me. "We're like two old, comfortable friends who know each other's jokes, know just what the other person is probably going to say."

The problem, Sara said, is that "when we're with other people, Ken is funny and charming, like the way he was with me years ago. But when we're alone, he acts bored and distracted. When I come home from a long day at work, his eyes just don't light up the way they used to."

Ken and Sara still had sex, but it became more mechanical and less frequent. Most depressing for Sara was the lack of romance or passion that Ken conveyed outside the bedroom.

There weren't any phone calls at the office any-more to say "I love you," no spontaneous kisses or hugs while she was in the kitchen making dinner. For a while, she'd dress herself up every Saturday night, imagin-ing "Ken would see me, sweep me off my feet, and take me out dancing." But he never did, and she'd fall asleep in front of the TV, feeling hurt and very angry.

After a year of feeling rejected, Sara became in-creasingly lonely and desperate.

"I tried everything from acting seductive to playing hard-to-get. It always ended the same. I'd lie awake at night, fantasizing he was whispering words of love and admiration in my ears."

Finally, Sara was able to tell Ken about her feel-ings. When she did, he initially got angry and ac-cused her of being overly demanding and needy. So she found that the only way to adjust was to become as emotionally cold as he was.

The days started feeling dull and lifeless after a while, as if she were just going through the motions. Things about Ken that used to seem endearing to her, like his slight stutter, now filled her with annoyance and contempt.

Sara told me in a flat, emotionless voice, "I'm 36 years old but I feel like 65, like my life is almost over. I know I used to be a soft, loving person, but that part of me seems gone."

WHY IS ROMANCE IMPORTANT?

Romance has become the most devalued aspect of life in today's psychology books. It's been called immature; nothing more than a prelude to genuine love, with no real value in itself; a dangerous smoke screen hiding the faults of one partner from the other.

Although these criticisms may be true to an extent, they don't tell the story of the importance of romance in a long-term relationship.

Marital romance, especially for the woman, is what connects the physical aspects of love (the body) to the spiritual aspects of love (the heart and soul). It shows the conscious decision of each partner to give selflessly and creatively to the other in an effort to keep the passion and life force of the marriage strong. It is the means by which your husband rededicates himself to you, affirms your significance, and lifts you out of your day-to-day mundane life.

Romance lets you and your husband keep a youthful energy, tenderness, excitement and sacredness in your relationship. In fact, the *Kabbalah* (the Jewish book of mysticism) teaches that the only way a man can achieve total personal development is to shower his wife with selfless devotion.

THE EFFECTS OF NO ROMANCE

The erosion of romance in a relationship is particularly painful to women for two main reasons.

Self-esteem: Women have been told for generations that they are mostly responsible for their relationship. We now live in a society where women are career women more than they are homemakers, where books and other media tell women they have the right to expect equal amounts of nurturing, affection and respect from their husbands. But despite this, many a woman continues to hear a small voice from the past telling her that it is she who must make her man happy. That if she expects too much, gives too little, he'll leave her for someone else.

This means that if you're coping with a loss of romance in your relationship, chances are you're also feeling a loss of self-esteem. You may assume that it must be because of some deficiency in you – that you're not attractive enough, exciting enough or lovable enough. A rejecting man can make you doubt all those good qualities in yourself about which you used to feel secure.

No other sense of purpose: Especially in the case of women who are homemakers – although it applies to working women, as well – much of their daily effort goes into creating a beautiful atmosphere for their husbands. If you are a homemaker and busy with shopping, cooking, paying bills, and planning activities for others, the one bright light you may look forward to at the end of the day is your husband's arrival. Thoughts of his affection, an intimate dinner or conversation and a romantic night out can give you the motivation to get through the most tedious day.

WHY DO SO MANY MEN HAVE SUCH A TOUGH TIME WITH ROMANCE AND INTIMACY?

Some men hold onto anger at their mothers for being either controlling and overpossessive, cold and rigid, or passive and weak. Once married, they unconsciously cast their wives into the role of their mothers. Then, when their wives come to them for nurturing, bonding or romance, they back off, out of fear of dependence or engulfment by "mother," or in order to retaliate against "mother" for his real mother's inadequate nurturing.

Also, some men just can't see the spiritual aspects to love and commitment. They may see being a husband as simply a role they have to take on, and romance as nothing more than a way to attract a wife.

HOW TO BUILD ROMANCE

● **Work hard on building the kind of self-esteem that comes from within.** You're far more desirable to a man when you're self-confident and happy. Although faking it doesn't work too long (it's hard to keep it up), it can work long enough for you to develop a real inner glow.

● **Love your body.** A romantic attitude starts with your believing that you're healthy, sexy and beautiful. If there are things about your body that you don't like but cannot change or are unable to change, learn to find them endearing and sensual in their own way. Be courageous in changing what you can, and start with good health. Let exercise, diet and the total nurturing of your body be your gift to yourself. Remember: When you don't like your body, you send off non-verbal signals to your partner that tell him not to look at you or touch you.

● **Dress to express.** Men are turned on by what they see far more than are women. (Think of the success of *Playboy* magazine compared to that of *Playgirl*!) No matter what your budget, find affordable clothes that are stylish, elegant and show off your passionate nature. And don't just dress up when you go out – dress up when you're home. When you dress sensually at home, you create a different aura.

● **Create a more sensual atmosphere at home.** Keep the TV off and the stereo on. Experiment with different kinds of music. Music stimulates passion, brings out emotions, and lifts you out of thinking about work. Light incense, use soft lighting in the bedroom, cover the bed with fluffy pillows, or eat by candlelight.

● **Organize, delegate and put housework in perspective so that it never interferes with your desire to have sex.** Men don't have fantasies about clean houses. It's far better to leave the cleaning until tomorrow than to give up an intimate moment.

● **Most men become automatically less romantic as a relationship grows older, even though their love for their partner may be as deep.** So you may have to assume the responsibility for keeping it alive, at least for a while.

Try these techniques:

❀ Fantasize more about your husband during the day, the way you did early in the relationship. Think back to your first kiss, the early flush of emotions. The more your desire is kept alive by this, the more he'll feel it.

❀ Tell him what you want sexually. Or write it in a note or card. A man loves to feel that he's exciting and fulfilling you.

❀ Change your look or style occasionally (hair, nails, clothes).

❀ Plan activities you can enjoy together to build intimacy and friendship.

❀ Be playful. Wrestle, giggle, watch funny movies together, do something fun like making love outdoors.

❀ Be sensual. Give each other massages, wash each other's hair.

❀ Plan lunch dates and "secret" meetings. Put sexy notes in his briefcase or lunch box. Keep him thinking of you and dreaming of you all day!

---

11. THE PURPOSE OF LIFE

Do you find yourself asking these questions?

❋ What's the real purpose of my life?

❋ Is there a higher reason for my suffering?

❋ Is there absolute truth, or are we free to decide what is moral and ethical?

❋ Will there ever be more to my life than this?

These are deep, spiritual questions. They show that you're trying to understand the meaning of your life or that you're trying to connect with something spiritual, something of lasting value.

Many women who suffer from the blues feel spiritually unfulfilled. Some have called this feeling "a lack of meaning", "a senselessness to live", and "a profound feeling of emptiness".

Ashley, an accountant and the mother of three children, told me, "It's like I'm searching for something that I realize my husband, children and job can't give me. And until I find it, a small part of me feels alone and very incomplete."

The search for meaning and spirituality can also cause the blues when you don't admit to and respect that search, but rather try to satisfy it some other way.

Some women cover up their lack of connection with their own spirituality by shopping.

> Clare, an admitted shopping addict, told me, "I would see a gorgeous dress that was more than I could afford, and I would think, 'If only I could buy it, then my wardrobe would be complete, and then I'd be able to feel complete.'"

Still other women cover up their spiritual needs through workaholism. Why the frantic need to fill time?

In his book, *I'd Like To Ask for Help But I Don't Know the Number*, Abraham Twerski, M.D., writes: "When all diversions are eliminated, we are left alone with ourselves, in direct contact with our human conditions and troubles..."

WHY ARE WOMEN PRONE TO THE SPIRITUAL BLUES?

First, women tend to be more thoughtful, more creative and more intuitive by nature. Therefore, the lack of a strong spiritual center is more upsetting or longed for in a woman than in a man.

Second, a woman's life tends to focus much more on spiritual matters than does that of a man. The menstrual cycle, the giving of life through childbirth, the teaching of spiritual and ethical values to children while Dad is at work, the creation of family and religious rituals at home...all these force her to constantly examine and deal with these profound questions.

94

FINDING SPIRITUALITY

Spirituality comes not just from feelings, but also from actions. It's not enough to simply "feel spiritual" or spend a few odd moments each day meditating. Instead, spirituality is about a set of principles you stand for. It's also about practice. In other words, your heart, thoughts and behaviors should be consistent.

Here are some guidelines for creating a spiritual life:

❀ Try to figure out your life's purpose and how you need to grow emotionally. You can identify these by closely examining your life and looking for patterns in your conflicts, fears and passions.

❀ Live each moment fully. When you're completely focused with passion on the task you're doing, no matter how boring it seems, you create a positive energy field that can actually double your energy and mental strength.

❀ Focus your energy on a manageable goal. In leading a spiritual life, you want to devote yourself to activities that will better mankind or the community. But if your goal is too large and outside your power, you'll ultimately become frustrated and give up. What's more, you'll turn off the people who really need you.

Instead, determine for yourself noble goals that are within your ability to reach. Remember, if you want to change the world or the people around you, you have to start with yourself. Put first things first, or you'll lose the things you cherish.

❀ As the 11th step of Alcoholics Anonymous teaches, seek conscious contact with God each day through prayer and meditation, asking for knowledge of God's will and the power to carry it out. This will center you and keep you focused on doing what's right and what's dignified. It will also let you see all that happens to you as part of a plan for your development and the development of those you love.

❀ Try to take the "I" out of things. The "I" is different from your legitimate need for respect and love. One way to guarantee that you're doing what's right is to ask yourself the question, "If my ego were not an issue for me, is this what I'd be saying or doing?"

Q.

Are there any herbs I can take for the blues?

A.

Herbs are natural medicines with energy- and mood-elevating powers. Here are a few to try:

Ginkgo (biloba):
Promotes blood circulation to the brain and boosts the manufacture of ATP, known as the universal energy molecules. Take 150 mg per day.

Siberian ginseng:
Helps metabolize the neurotransmitters serotonin and acetylcholine as well as increase activity of lymphocytes, which help the immune system. Follow directions on package.

Melatonin:
Improves sleep to prevent fatigue during the day. Follow directions on package.

Chinese adaptogenic herbs:
Including astragalus and echinacea, which support the immune system. Follow directions on package.

12. BODY CHEMISTRY

Sadly, even the most secure of childhoods and the most loving relationship can't guarantee that a person won't suffer from the blues. That's because many people's bodies manufacture too little or too much of certain neurochemicals.

For these people, psychiatrists recommend medication. Doctors used to prescribe three main types of antidepressant drugs: tricyclics; monoamine oxidase inhibitors (MAOIs); and lithium (for manic-depression and some recurring, major depression). Unfortunately, patients who took them suffered uncomfortable side effects.

Now, there are new antidepressants that have few of the side effects associated with the traditional drugs. SSRIs (serotonin-specific reuptake inhibitors) work to increase one of the major brain messengers, *serotonin*. Another type acts on the neurotransmitter *dopamine*.

The vast majority of women, however, will benefit from the strategies and suggestions we've discussed in this book. We wish you the best of luck. You definitely deserve it.

Brian F. Greer, M.D.

Carla Hreer